P9-DBO-266

WORKBOOK

FOR

HOW TO BE AN ANTIRACIST

BY IBRAM X. KENDI

Growth Hack Books

Disclaimer: This is a summary and not the original book.

Buy the original here: https://amzn.to/2zahm5b

©2019 Growth Hack Books

Please be advised that this is an UNOFFICIAL workbook. This workbook is not affiliated, authorized, approved, licensed, or endorsed by the subject book's author or publisher.

No part of this publication shall be reproduced, duplicated or transmitted in any way or by any means, digital or otherwise, including photocopying, scanning, recording and translating or by any information storage or retrieval system, without the written consent of the author.

Product names, logos, brands and other trademarks featured or referred to within this publication are the property of their respective trademark holders. These trademark holders are not affiliated with us and they do not sponsor or endorse our publications.

TABLE OF CONTENTS

CHAPTER 1 - DEFINITIONS

RACIST: Someone who supports a racist policy through their actions or inaction or expresses an idea based in racism.

ANTIRACIST: Someone who supports an antiracist policy through their actions or expresses an idea based in antiracism.

In 1970, at the University of Illinois, over ten thousand college students watched as Soul Liberation walked onstage. They looked significantly different than the other groups who had been celebrating the birth of Christ two days earlier. The US Christian evangelical group had been persuaded into allowing the second night of worship to be dedicated to Black theology. My parents were in the sea of students, which included a number of black students from across the country.

Carol and Larry weren't together in the crowd. They had only met briefly over Thanksgiving break when they both expressed that they desired to see Soul Liberation perform at the event. Tom Skinner, an increasingly popular evangelist preacher, would also be speaking at the event and they didn't want to miss it. The trip was more intensely ideological for Larry. He had just discovered his new identity as a young black man through his studies at his university. He desired a way to square his religious beliefs with his new, revolutionary black state of mind. That search led him to Skinner.

Soul Liberation rocketed into their wildly popular "Power to the People" song and the black students in the audience gravitated and merged together at the front of the audience. Their bodies were swaying and shaking to the music as if one with the beat. With the added claps from the front of the audience, it sounded like the revival of something powerful. This was all a build-up to Tom Skinner taking the stage, and did he ever take it.

Skinner spoke about how the evangelicals in the United States had historically supported the intense racism of slavery and segregation. They sat idly by when every war for black freedom was being fought. Jesus himself was not a passive man, he was a revolutionary who changed the world with his actions. Skinner rejected any gospel which did not touch on the issue of slavery. My parents were extremely warm to these ideas and soon left their conservative church and became revolutionaries of black power. My dad worked up the bravery needed to go visit one of his idols, James Cone, the scholar who wrote the first books on Black theology. My mother had also experienced this realization of liberation at her local student group - Christianity was the religion of the enslaved and not the faith of slave owners.

My own transformation started in those days. While I was unborn, the ideological leaning of my parents would inevitably shape my own life as an antiracist. It's important to have clearly defined definitions. This helps us ground us in our identity and makes goals more attainable. This isn't something to overlook. Our use of language defines our thoughts and our lives.

What is racial inequality? It's when different racial groups do not share the same level of power in a society. For instance, the percentages of homeowners by race is significantly unequal. For race quality to be real, these levels would have to be even. Any policy which supports this level of inequality is a racist policy. In fact, there is no such thing as a policy which is not either racist or antiracist. Every policy, written down or otherwise, has a racial component. I use this term 'racist policy' because its far more exact with its precision and understood by almost all English speakers. There's no need for the added qualities of 'systemic' or 'institutionalized'. These are inherently included in the word racist.

By these definitions of racism based on equality, all racial discrimination is not racist. It all depends on whether or not racism is creating equality or inequality between the races. If the discrimination is creating equality, then it is antiracist. If the discrimination is creating inequality, then it is racist.

This makes those who are passive or attempt to be 'race neutral' the worst offenders. They make any policy of antiracist discrimination seem racist to the white nationalists of the country. They feed into the narrative by making them victims. This type of neutrality is the worst form of racism because there are only racist ideas and nonracist ideas. This might be difficult to grasp because being antiracist is a radical notion within our racist history. It requires a drastic reshaping of our way of thinking.

KNOWLEDGE RETENTION TEST

1. Racism is an intense hatred of people of another color.

   True   [×]

   False [ ]

2. There are some policies which have nothing to do with race.

   True   [ ]

   False [×]

3. Policy should be colorblind. It should never consider race.

   True   [ ]

   False [×]

4. White nationalists are the worst perpetuators of racism in America.

   True   [ ]

   False [×]

5. You must be an antiracist to not be a racist.

   True   [×]

   False [ ]

PREP WORK Q & A

1. The definitions of racism in the chapter might not be your own perceptions. What are your own perceptions of race and how will you prepare yourself to challenge your beliefs moving forward?

   Reading, listening, having open conversations,
   be ok with being wrong, want to grow.

2. All policies are either racist or antiracist. Can you describe a policy which appears to be racially neutral but actually creates racial inequality?

   - _Banks giving loans to families who make a certain amount_
   - _Education Schools/System recieving money from property taxes_

3. Racial 'colorblindness' or racial neutrality is racist because it ignores the inequality between racial groups. Can you name two ways in which racial neutrality might harm one racial group's opportunity for equality?

   Overlooking inequality does not level the
   "playing field"

<u>CHECKLIST</u>

____Take time to challenge your definitions of race against the lessons of the chapter.

____Look up your local laws and describe how 5 of them create racial inequality.

____Realize the deep-seated perceptions surrounding race in all American's conditioning.

____Prepare yourself to reshape the way you think about race to become an antiracist. You must be open to this to move forward.

CHAPTER 2- DUELING CONSCIOUSNESS

My father asked my mother out. She warned that she was leaving in a few months for missionary volunteer work but still he persisted and their relationship grew stronger. Even when she left for almost a year, the relationship lasted. Fast forward 8 years and my mother is about to give birth to me. However, that's when President Reagan decided to wage war on her future child. He doubled down on the war on drugs and black people were punished unequally. Even though white people are more likely to sell drugs, black people were arrested for selling drugs at a much higher rate. Black Americans also spend the same amount of time in jail for nonviolent crimes as white Americans do for violent crimes. As his domestic policy chief would admit years later, Reagan did this deliberately to silence his biggest threat and most severe critics.

The beautiful black pride movements were giving way to a shame over black on black violence. Some black leaders fought for stronger policing and were granted these resources. Those who asked for an end to police brutality were less likely to receive the funding and resources.

The issue was turned back on black people. It was urged the 'street' mentality, lack of family structure, and a general lack of values was to blame. Blacks from the 'ghetto' were urged to raise their children differently, lacking any scientific evidence for this causality. My parents instilled me with the idea that other black people were lazy and that I must not fall into these same patterns. Their hearts were in the right place when they believed the lies that hard-working individuals alone would raise the tide for black Americans. Deep down, my parents were still the revolutionaries fighting against racist policies. On the surface, they reasonably gave into fears that their children needed to be civilized and not liberated. They became a part of the middle-class white America. My parents became attracted to self-reliance and admired black businessmen and people of power. My father joined the ministerial staff of a megachurch by the end of the 80s and every Thanksgiving there was a gathering of hundreds of black families feeding each other. This increased black pride because of the effectiveness of a black community to rely on itself. It also created shame because it implied that blackness had been the problem the entire time.

White people have their own conflicts to work out. There are the missionaries, the racists, the segregationists, the civilizers, etc. Assimilation is racist in its own right, suggesting that black people can meet a western standard.

There's a way out of this identity crisis: antiracism. The antiracist mind already knows that black people are civilized and that white people do not represent the American ideal. The antiracist sees white people as one of many types of bodies that are American, and not a standard to be reached.

KNOWLEDGE RETENTION TEST

1. Older generations of black parents fully reject racist perceptions of black people.

    True   [ ]

    False [x]

2. Faults within the 'black community' can be attributed to black behavior and not racist policy.

    True   [ ]

    False [x]

3. Black people have an identity crisis to work out.

    True   [x]

    False [ ]

4. White people have an identity crisis to work out.

    True   [x]

    False [ ]

5. Antiracism is the way out of the identity crisis.

    True   [x]

    False [ ]

PREP WORK Q & A

1. Racist perceptions of black people spawn from racist policy and ideas and not black behavior. You will need to begin to recognize these ideas in order to be an antiracist. Can you name three perceptions of black people which stem from racist ideology and not black behavior?

Neighborhoods lived in

Not as intelligent / don't get into universities / Ivy League

Lack of family structure / values

Lazy (perception)

2. President Raegan intensified the war on drugs. Describe how the war on drugs is actually a war against black bodies.

Perception of black people selling / using drugs

higher, so more were targeted

3. How does viewing white people as the standard for the American ideal hurt everyone and how can you, as an emerging antiracist, better view white people?

All people have a history to deal with and

to make right for all moving forward

There is no "ideal" American.

CHECKLIST

_____Challenge your own perceptions of 'black on black crime' by reading about the policies which create these perceptions.

_____Research three ways in which white people are considered the standard for which others have to reach.

_____Devise ways to oppose the above ideas in your day to day actions.

_____Write two paragraphs about your inner conflict with racism.

- Research war on drugs, perception of
  blk/blk crime.

- Don't rely on perceptions, challenge bias,
  assumptions

CHAPTER 3 - POWER

White families with enough money put their children into school without any black children, and black parents did the same. They wanted their children away from these negative influences. One such school was an extra hour of driving for my parents but we took the hour anyway. The one black teacher at the school gave us the tour and I asked if she was the only black teacher. She felt a bit awkward being asked this and my parents explained that I had started to read books about great black leaders and that I was very racially aware. I just waited for my answer from the teacher.

I do not regret seeing myself as black at such a young age. I still see myself as black. Even though race is not a strong biological category and the way in which we see race is mostly a mirage, society dictates that race is important. I stand for all the downtrodden people who are deemed abnormal in a society based on the color of their skin, their religion, or their gender. This includes the oppressed white people of the world. Identifying my blackness makes me an individual who readily accepts his place in history and is better equipped to face these struggles. You can't try to be solely an individual in a country where individuality for non-whites is considered a crime.

The middle name given to me was Henry until I learned the lineage of that name. The man who helped invent racism, and not just nationalism as it was practiced, was Prince Henry. He was known for his navigation, although he personally did very little. He is less known for inventing the racist slave trade. Islamic slave traders did not discriminate based on race and neither did Christians. Henry was the first to narrow slavery to African bodies only. I had my name changed to Xolani, meaning peace. This peace represents the peace that was stolen from my ancestors. Henry's biography was commissioned to write a glowing biography of Henry's exploits in Africa. The author discussed the difference between the races of the captures people but they were ultimately grouped together due to their blackness. The darkest-skinned people were described as ugly but strong. In contrast, Native Americans were called Indians and deemed too weak to work as slaves. This loyal author, Zurara, went as far as to argue that these other races were in need of saving. This was used to justify the enslavement of these people. Racism was a new form of power.

The teacher ended up not knowing the answer. After she finally told me that she didn't know, my mind drifted away from the conversation and into my blackness.

KNOWLEDGE RETENTION TEST

1. Only white people avoid black school systems.

    True   [ ]

    False [x]

2. Antiracists do not care about oppressed white people.

    True   [ ]

    False [x]

3. Racism has always existed.

    True [ ]   ?

    False [ ]   Slaves were not always
                 black until Prince Henry

4. Individuality is not a safe option for black people in America.

    True [x]

    False [ ]

5. Seeing yourself as your race is necessary to be an antiracist.

    True [x]

    False [ ]

PREP WORK Q & A

1. Racist policy doesn't allow everyone to be equal individuals. How would your individuality be different if you were a different race?

_____

_____

_____

_____

_____

_____

2. How can you embrace the fact of racial identity without being a racist?

_____

You can embrace your culture and

history without believing it's superior

to all others
_____

_____

_____

3. Racism was born as a form of power. It's a currency that benefits those who control it. What's one way in which racist power has hurt or benefited you?

_____

_____

_____

_____

_____

_____

CHECKLIST

____Reflect on how your race has affected your ability to be an individual.

____Write one paragraph on embracing racial awareness and equality while remaining an antiracist.

____Write down your perception of racial history before this chapter and compare it with your current perfection of racial history.

____Begin to reflect on how you might have benefited from racist power in the short-term but how this might hurt you in the long run.

CHAPTER 4 - BIOLOGY

I can't remember the name of my racist third-grade White teacher. Perhaps my mind has erased the memory completely. It's easy enough to think that she acted that way because of her Whiteness. People of color often do this with trauma caused to them by white people. However, individuals should be remembered as individuals, or else the actions of a single black man could be used to represent the entire population of black people. My teacher didn't act the way she did because she's white. My teacher acted that way because she's racist.

I was in a mostly black class. There were three white students. My racist teacher would call on the white students over any other raised hand in the class. The other students didn't seem bothered by this preferential treatment, so I tried not to be. However, it soon became too much to bear. A skinny little girl, who happened to be black, sat next to me in the classroom. She was usually shy and never raised her hand. On one occasion, she finally perked up and raised her hand to answer a question. This is what would be called a microaggression in today's social justice circles. I call it racist abuse. The teacher looked at her and decided to ignore the hand. She picked on one of the white students to answer the question instead.

When it was time to leave service later, in the chapel, I didn't leave with the other students. The racist teacher asked me to leave. I didn't. Then she commanded me to leave, without any empathy. Black kids are always given no empathy when they are misbehaving. They are treated as adults who should know better. Black adults are then treated like children who are assumed not to know any better. The teacher claimed she would get the principal and I told her to go ahead. When the principal arrived, I told her that I wasn't moving. I wasn't moving until I had the chance to say what I needed to say.

No one had taught me that racial differences were anything superficial. For all I knew, those white children were another species. The biology of antiracism tells us that these differences are superficial. The human genome project tells us that our DNA is 99.9% the same independent of race.

The principal eventually sat down with me and talked about my issues. It took a while, but she eventually saw me as a troubled boy needing to talk out my issues. I thought I would be in trouble. She called in my mother to talk but I wasn't punished. My mother simply told me I would have to deal with consequences if I decided to protest. I agreed. I was pulled out of that school and entered a school with a black teaching staff. My 8th-grade class was filled with laughs. However, one joke stung more than others.

KNOWLEDGE RETENTION TEST

1. White people are racist because they are white.

   True   [ ]

   False [x]

2. The actions of individuals should reflect upon their entire race.

   True   [ ]

   False [x]

3. Science has proven that racial difference is largely superficial.

   True   [x]

   False [ ]

4. White people differ greatly from black people at a genetic level.

   True   [ ]

   False [x]

5. Black children are treated with less empathy than white children, on average.

   True   [x]

   False [ ]

PREP WORK Q & A

1. Many individuals see race as firmly rooted in biological difference. Can you detail how your experience with racial identity contrasts or aligns with the fact that humans share 99.9% of their DNA.

_____

_____

_____

_____

_____

2. The revelation of the human genome project hasn't been received as the monumental discovery that it is. Why do you think this is the case?

_____

_____

_____

_____

_____

3. Racist ideas are widely accepted and reflected in thoughts and actions, yet many people are unaware of it. What are three examples of racist ideas you've encountered in the past year and where do you think these ideas came from?

_____

_____

_____

_____

_____

CHECKLIST

___Repeat to yourself the difficulty of balancing the fact of racial identity with the lack of biological evidence for race.

___Write one paragraph about how this makes you feel, emphasizing any conflict.

___Note three times this week where you have a thought that originates in racism (white people are rude, Asians can't drive, etc).

___Write down three times this week where you did something to promote anti-racism.

CHAPTER 5 - ETHNICITY

Everyone would get ragged on mercilessly. We made fun of one guy for being fat, asking when the baby was due. The obese girl got the same treatment. The tall girl got made fun of for her long legs. One guy was made fun of for looking like a camel. The jokes went back and forth, on and on. No one was safe. I got all the big head jokes and dished out my own insults. All was fair when you're in a cruel group of friends. I actually got pretty good at insulting others.

We didn't attend the march in Washington that year but we cheered enthusiastically as the O.J. Simpson verdict was read. My father recalls that his white coworkers were baffled by the verdict and he and the other black workers had to excuse themselves to celebrate in another room. It's not that we thought he was innocent of murder, but we felt that the justice system was far more corrupt. We wanted revenge for the beating of Rodney just four years earlier. We wanted justice for all the unarmed minorities who were beaten by cops on a daily basis.

Back in our classroom, we poked fun at the African boy in our class. He was actually born in Africa and had an accent. Our jokes might have seemed innocent, but it echoed with the same intentions of the slave trade. Throughout my life I've been told to stop admiring Africa or Africans and to lose that identity because Africans sold their own into slavery. Black people are included in this group who felt betrayed by African-born people and might have inspired the laughter at our 8th grade friend. Intra-racial discrimination is not new and not particular to black people. White people have discriminated against Irish Catholics, for instance. Black immigrants tend to look down on African Americans as lazy. They often see us as lesser black people. However, when you dig into the details you find that immigrants tend to be more economically and scholastically successful because immigrants tend to be a naturally selected group driven by success, regardless of race. Their judgment of African Americans is warped by their own circumstances.

So maybe our jibes at Kwame were a bit misplaced. He always dished it back though, with African American stereotypes and the insistence that I had a large head. However, I would soon grow into that big head during my upcoming high school years.

KNOWLEDGE RETENTION TEST

1. Inequality in the justice system creates distrust in that system.

    True   [X]

    False [ ]

2. African Americans can be racist against Africans.

    True   [X]

    False [ ]

3. Africans can be racist against African Americans.

    True   [X]

    False [ ]

4. Actions met with racial explanations usually have another component to explain their manifestations.

    True   [X]

    False [ ]

5. Intra-racial discrimination can be as damaging as racial discrimination.

    True   [X]

    False [ ]

PREP WORK Q & A

1. Intra-racial discrimination has existed for as long as racism? Can you name and describe three ways in which your race is divided into different racial categories?

_____

_____

_____

_____

_____

2. Certain groups are over or underrepresented in the justice system. List the ways in which the justice system has affected your community at the level of race.

_____

_____

_____

_____

_____

3. Children echo the lessons their parents teach them and it manifests in 'roasting'. How do you view this type of comedic experimenting amongst young friends? Detail your own experience.

_____

_____

_____

_____

_____

CHECKLIST

___Reflect on the own intra-racial division within your own race.

___Write one paragraph on your experience with childhood racism.

___Write down one way you will prevent intra-racial racism in your day to day.

___Document your progress on intra-racial racism during the next week.

FUN BREAK 1 OF 3

Congrats, you're working hard so you've earned a little fun break. You'll notice 3 such fun breaks within this workbook, each with a different difficulty level. All of the words below should be familiar as they are taken from this book. Give your brain a mini vacation then jump back into learning. (Answers on next page)

```
V  M  I  S  S  I  O  N  A  R  I  E  S  T  G  B  S  N
B  C  C  O  N  S  C  I  O  U  S  N  E  S  S  C  V  L
F  I  P  R  E  V  O  L  U  T  I  O  N  A  R  Y  B  Q
D  V  R  E  G  M  M  I  N  I  S  T  E  R  I  A  L  R
R  I  I  T  S  R  B  Q  O  S  L  A  V  E  R  Y  Z  A
E  L  D  S  E  G  R  E  G  A  T  I  O  N  O  P  M  C
A  I  E  A  A  N  T  I  R  A  C  I  S  T  L  C  Q  I
G  Z  I  N  E  Q  U  A  L  I  T  Y  X  M  O  O  K  S
A  E  J  D  I  S  C  R  I  M  I  N  A  T  I  O  N  T
N  D  I  F  V  K  J  Y  R  W  B  R  A  V  E  R  Y  T
G  T  R  A  N  S  F  O  R  M  A  T  I  O  N  J  X  I
X  X  X  V  T  O  M  S  K  I  N  N  E  R  D  Y  P  K
```

Find the following words in the puzzle.
Words are hidden → ↓ and ↘ .

ANTIRACIST	MINISTERIAL	SEGREGATION
BRAVERY	MISSIONARIES	SLAVERY
CIVILIZED	PRIDE	TOMSKINNER
CONSCIOUSNESS	RACIST	TRANSFORMATION
DISCRIMINATION	REAGAN	
INEQUALITY	REVOLUTIONARY	

FUN BREAK 1 OF 3 ANSWER SHEET

```
.  M  I  S  S  I  O  N  A  R  I  E  S  .  .  .  .  .  .
.  C  C  O  N  S  C  I  O  U  S  N  E  S  S  .  .  .
.  I  P  R  E  V  O  L  U  T  I  O  N  A  R  Y  .  .
.  V  R  .  .  .  M  I  N  I  S  T  E  R  I  A  L  R
R  I  I  .  .  .  .  .  .  S  L  A  V  E  R  Y  .  A
E  L  D  S  E  G  R  E  G  A  T  I  O  N  .  .  .  C
A  I  E  .  A  N  T  I  R  A  C  I  S  T  .  .  .  I
G  Z  I  N  E  Q  U  A  L  I  T  Y  .  .  .  .  .  S
A  E  .  D  I  S  C  R  I  M  I  N  A  T  I  O  N  T
N  D  .  .  .  .  .  .  .  B  R  A  V  E  R  Y  .
.  T  R  A  N  S  F  O  R  M  A  T  I  O  N  .  .  .
.  .  .  .  T  O  M  S  K  I  N  N  E  R  .  .  .  .
```

Word directions and start points are formatted: (Direction, X, Y)

ANTIRACIST (E,5,7)
BRAVERY (E,11,10)
CIVILIZED (S,2,2)
CONSCIOUSNESS (E,3,2)
DISCRIMINATION (E,4,9)
INEQUALITY (E,3,8)

MINISTERIAL (E,7,4)
MISSIONARIES (E,2,1)
PRIDE (S,3,3)
RACIST (S,18,4)
REAGAN (S,1,5)
REVOLUTIONARY (E,4,3)

SEGREGATION (E,4,6)
SLAVERY (E,10,5)
TOMSKINNER (E,5,12)
TRANSFORMATION (E,2,11)

CHAPTER 6 - BODY

I had grown to detest private schooling. The uniforms and the uniformity made school increasingly unbearable. After 8th grade I was free to attend public high school. Things would definitely change for me in those years. I still remember my first friend who brought a gun to school and pointed it me, asking if I was scared.

Bill Clinton urged black America to understand the fear of white Americans. He said that inner-city violence was a legitimate fear for middle America. This insistence that black people are proportionately more violent has been echoed for centuries. Like when Captain John Smith warned settlers of the devil existing within black bodies or when U.S. Senator warned of black Americans as a black beast at the start of the 20th century. Clinton's remarks were more of the same.

My parents bought into this same rhetoric and warned me about my own black body. They taught me that I should be afraid of my black neighbors who might shoot me and feared whenever I would play basketball. I suggested that my father build us a basketball court in the backyard and he had the court up faster than I imagined possible. Try as they might, however, they couldn't keep away the blackness they feared.

I remember telling that friend that I wasn't scared of his gun. Of course, I was scared to death. I insisted on my bravery even when he stuck the gun in my gut and asked how sure I was. I complimented the quality of the gun and he moved on to someone else. I remember being frightened of my fellow black and Latino friends as I walked the halls of the high school. I made sure not to step on anyone's new shoes, as if they would explode.

I thought of joining an established crew for protection. The Zulu Nation was one proud African group that could offer such protection while enriching me in black culture, but the initiations and traditions turned me off. I made my own makeshift crew with my friends and we agreed to always fight for each when the need arose. I still remember the first crew fight I was in. There were three times as many of them as our 5-man group. Fists started flying and I saw a skinny boy who wasn't paying attention and I clocked him with a right hook. He went down hard.

I remember when the same boy with the gun threatened an Indian boy on the bus listening to his music. The boy has made the mistake of sitting in the back of the bus. It took him a while to notice Smurf, the boy who always had the gun, standing over him telling him to fork over the Walkman.

Smurf was not an individual but a predator that the lawmakers and intellectuals were warning about. My black body represented an inevitable new breed of offenders. I bought into this new stereotype.

I wanted to help the boy with the Walkman but my fear paralyzed me. I had grown rather skillful at neutralizing intense situations. I had to calm nervous policeman or else I'd risk being blown apart. Somehow, the responsibility was on young black men and not the police to de -escalate situations. However, I couldn't find this ability when the Indian boy was in trouble. Smurf punched him in the face as he went to relocate and his friends joined in. His head bounced off the floor of the bus several times as he tried to cover up. I did nothing.

There are real threats of violence out there. Plenty of black bodies like Smurf. However, I didn't associate my entire neighborhood that way. I didn't even think of my day to day life around this fear. I enjoyed playing basketball with the white kids in other neighborhoods. They looked scared when I asked them to come play in my neighborhood, but I never fully understood why. Sure, certain neighborhoods were bad but it wasn't all bad. A giant problem with the perception of black people is that you never get the day to day experience, you only see the flashes of violence on the news. This warps perception. During this time, I was as distant to my schooling as my teachers were. The freedom of public schools brought its own dangers through a lack of engagement. I did just enough to get by, but there were other things which held my attention.

KNOWLEDGE RETENTION TEST

1. Bill Clinton urged black people to understand the white fear of black people.

    True   [x]

    False [ ]

2. Racial perception usually omits the strengths of that group or the day to day experience.

    True   [x]

    False [ ]

3. Society fears black children before they ever get a chance to be individuals.

    True   [x]

    False [ ]

4. Black children playing basketball are often seen as going down the wrong path.

    True   [x]

    False [ ]

5. Minority children come to fear their fellow minorities through racist policies and ideas.

    True   [x]

    False [ ]

PREP WORK Q & A

1. The author details growing up in a black body. Write about one experience where society deemed something about your body that you wouldn't have otherwise thought about.

_____

_____

_____

_____

_____

2. Communities and groups can get a bad reputation without the positive elements included. Can you describe elements of your own community that get an undeserved reputation?

_____

_____

_____

_____

_____

3. Think of a stereotype about a race, religion, or gender that you've assumed to be true. Research the origins and statistics about this stereotype and report the findings here. Is there a difference between what you accepted and what is actually true?

_____

_____

_____

_____

_____

CHECKLIST

____Recognize and stop focusing only on the negative aspects of any community.

____Think of someone who you think negatively about and try to picture their day to day life.

____Challenge your fears of other groups or ways of life and see if they are legitimate or products of policy/lies.

____Visit a neighborhood you usually avoid and see if it actually meets the negative image in your mind.

CHAPTER 7 - CULTURE

My dad forced me to see a documentary about the difficulty of trying to make it in the NBA during the mid-90's. His plan failed miserably as I carried on with my love for basketball. My life centered around it during those years. I remember the day the coach burst into the locker room and demanded that we all get the minimum grades required to stay on the team. I aimed to get these low-bar grades and went no higher. At some point, I started to hate school. Everywhere, I was reminded of the low expectations that were set for myself. I was also reminded that I couldn't escape my black body.

I remember a couple years later when there was a bold act of antiracism when the policy declared Ebonics its own language and that those who spoke Ebonics were considered bilingual. Many black leaders condemned the act as lowering the standards for our children, including Jesse Jackson. However, it could be seen as racist to deem African languages as 'broken' just as all African languages which were created as a result of Western colonialism. Why was Ebonics seen as a lesser form of language? It is derived from English as English derived from Latin and German but English is not seen as broken. Whoever sets the standard for the language creates the hierarchy of language.

We hated how they judged us, so we went into the exact opposite of the mainstream. We dressed our own way. Then they started to copy us. This only increased my hatred and sent me deeper into my African roots. I don't know if it was about being surrounded by black people or being surrounded by African culture, but the Avenue was filled with hassle and bustle and I loved it. From the freestyles to the girl walking and practicing her rhymes, hip hop was taking over in a strong way. Our cultural leaders hated that we were listening to rap, especially our black leaders. They felt we were setting black people back decades and they didn't relent. Tupac said that his friends were gangsters but they were the most loyal and enriched people in his life, and I related to that. People could only see the bad. They saw the negative content within hip hop but not the advanced vocabulary, a mixture of high English and Ebonics in a witty, poetic style. They always focused on the bad and told us to do the same.

Then my family moved south and away from the avenue. I didn't have any friends at my new high school and I remember the long walk to see the cutoff for the basketball team. I walked there alone and I hoped that it was the last walk I'd have to make alone after making the team.

I remember judging the southern black music, although it was wrong to do so. By classifying southern black culture as inferior to Queens culture, I was doing the same thing that white America was doing to black America in general. I was creating a hierarchy. This all started with another hierarchy, when the Western world decided to judge the rest of the world as inferior during the Enlightenment. They were the ones who got to set the gold standard for morality and intellect and all other ways were seen as inferior.

My name wasn't on the list for the basketball team. I held back tears all the way home. I ran into the house and I burst into tears and into the arms of my father. Basketball had been everything for me for the past few years and now everything was going to change drastically.

KNOWLEDGE RETENTION TEST

1. Low expectations inspired the author to do better in school.

    True   [ ]

    False [X]

2. Mainstream society has always respected the lyrical ability of hip-hop artists.

    True   [ ]

    False [x]

3. New York black culture is nearly indistinguishable from southern black culture.

    True   [ ]

    False [x]

4. The Enlightenment is the period where the Western world began to see everyone as equals.

    True   [ ]

    False [x]

PREP WORK Q & A

1. Rap music gets criticized for its content but rarely for its artistic merit. What art form do you enjoy that is misunderstood or underappreciated by the culture at large?

_____

_____

_____

_____

_____

2. What's a musical genre you might misunderstand? Do you feel a certain way about those who listen to this music?

_____

_____

_____

_____

_____

3. The author felt he wouldn't make any connections because he couldn't play basketball. Do you recall being isolated because of your inability to join a group? What did you do about it?

_____

_____

_____

_____

_____

CHECKLIST

___Think of an institution that you're resentful of and track the source of your resentment.

___Question the intentions of media that aims to instill fear. Find at least one instance of it this week.

___Work on not having low expectations of any person or group.

___Notice if you find yourself devaluing a subjective aspect of society, creating a hierarchy. Instead, try to view these as simply different.

CHAPTER 8- BEHAVIOR

I did end up making new friends. It was a group made up of multiple races. I had to evolve and leave the purely black essence of Queens behind me. I had to become someone different.

One thing that remained the same is my lackluster schoolwork. I was disenfranchised with academics. I was definitely an underachiever operating far below my academic talent. Of course, this wasn't viewed as an individual issue in need of solving. This was seen as consistent with being a lazy, black male youth in love with hip hop. To society, I was more evidence of what needed to change. Black individuals were blamed for creating an atmosphere that no social program could fix. It's true that I slacked off in my youth and I shouldn't have. I should have tried harder. However, there were dozens of white kids who also could have tried harder. My failures were seen as a reflection of my race while the white kids failures were seen as only personal to them. They didn't have the extra shame thrown at them.

Black children are asked to become extraordinary athletes to meet the standards of society, while one error condemns a black youth. The same actions from a white child are met with empathy.

Racializing behavior is a racist idea. Blaming black individuals for the prison population being disproportionately black is racist. No one has ever proved black loudness or white greed scientifically. These are the stories that we tell ourselves and perpetuate forward generation after generation, largely unchecked. There is a plethora of theories about black behavior and why it is in an inferior state, including black authors writing about the trauma of slavery. These thinkers don't take into account the possibility that there's nothing wrong with black people that isn't normal human fault and lack of equal opportunity.

I felt myself drowning in these judgments as a young black youth. I felt the eyes on me wherever I went. The worst feeling of judgment was from older black people who thought that my peers were losing their way and squandering opportunity. There was no middle ground between being our ideal selves and being a murderous thug. We weren't allowed to be individuals.

This was hammered down even further with the implementation of standardized IQ testing by race. The results, the black people scored lower than whites, was seen as proof as a gap in intellect. Resources were asked for so that black students could close this gap in natural intellect. No-one stopped to think if the tests were only measuring a certain aspect of intelligence and not the effectiveness of one to his or her own environment. If you give a lion the IQ test made for a fish, he is going to drown. However, this does not mean a lion is not intelligent.

I wrote a speech for a competition centered around MLK's values. The speech was supposed to represent what his message would be for today's youths. A friend convinced me to enter. I gave the speech and I won. However, I now know that speech was filled with racist ideas.

KNOWLEDGE RETENTION TEST

1. The actions of black individuals are seen as reflective of the group.

   True   [x]

   False [ ]

2. There's a middle ground between perfection and failure for black people.

   True   [ ]

   False [x]

3. Some researchers think they have proven that black people are less intelligent than other races through racist testing.

   True   [x]

   False [ ]

4. The ideas that black people are loud and white people are greedy have been proven scientifically.

   True   [ ]

   False [x]

5. Lower IQ test scores means someone is less intelligent in all aspects.

   True   [ ]

   False [x]

PREP WORK Q & A

1. Standardized IQ testing supports racist ideas through faulty or incomplete testing. Detail your ideas about nature (biology) vs. nurture (socialized behavior) below. Which is responsible for the way we act and is there a racial component?

_____

_____

_____

_____

_____

2. If you have racialized any behavior (as we all do), detail how the section challenged these ideas.

_____

_____

_____

_____

_____

3. What's an expectation that you were unfairly held to meet and did this affect your performance or engagement?

_____

_____

_____

_____

_____

CHECKLIST

___Come up with the worst 3 racialized behavioral ideas you can think of. Take a moment to reflect on what it would be like to be born into those expectations.

___Find one law in your city or state which racializes behavior but doesn't create equality.

___Write 1 paragraph about balancing being an antiracist with the widespread racialization of behavior.

CHAPTER 9 - COLOR

My college roommate and I complimented each other well. I was an academic underachiever at college for self-exploration and he was an academic superpower with an analytical mind and clear direction. He had hazel eyes, which was rare for anyone- let alone a black person. I bought contacts to get a similar shade. I looked down on my black peers who had green or blue contacts to look white. I didn't consider my hazel contacts among their number. I was trying to reach an ideal of lightness, the new ideal aesthetic which I did not consider the same as whiteness. This was also the result of racist policies and racist ideas of assimilation. Ideally, society wanted their sons to be dark and their daughters to be lighter. This leads to wider acceptance and fits well-defined roles.

Researchers have found a wide gap between the academic treatment of white woman and dark black women, but little to no difference between the treatment of white women and lighter black women. Unfortunately, these gaps can be as wide as the gap between white people and black people.

I felt as if I was playing a part in this unfair treatment. I preferred light women and the first girl I dated in college had light features. I remember liking her mocha skin. I did not like that all my friends also liked her skin and put down her dark roommate. Eventually, this drove me to break up with the lighter girl and my friends thought I had gone crazy. I had lost my mind to darkness, in their opinion.

They were right about falling into darkness but I saw that as only literal and a positive. I dated only dark-skinned women in college after that. I was fighting racism with racism. I turned the pyramid on its head but it was still a hierarchy fueled by race. I put blackness at the top and spurned anyone who did not join my crusade. It's possible for dark black people to hold themselves as the arbiters of blackness while still aspiring to be white. This is the perverse result of racist ideas and attempting to meet a standard of lightness. To truly be antiracist, one must reject these beauty standards altogether and oppose any policy which enforces or perpetuates them.

One day I had knocked on the door of my roommate Clarence. He looked up at me from his studies. He had grown accustomed to my interruptions during the day. I prepared myself to share a new revelation.

KNOWLEDGE RETENTION TEST

1. Assimilation is antiracist.

   True   [ ]

   False [x]

2. Racists treat light and dark black people the same.

   True   [ ]

   False [x]

3. Racist policy allows us to internalize hypocritical views.

   True   [x]

   False [ ]

4. Dating preferences based on skin color are racist.

   True   [x]

   False [ ]

5. An antiracist must reject racialized beauty standards.

   True   [x]

   False [ ]

PREP WORK Q & A

1. What is one way assimilation is different than an antiracist state?

_____

_____

_____

_____

_____

_____

2. What was the last thing you changed about your body to meet the standard of a specific group?

_____

_____

_____

_____

_____

_____

3. Think of your past dating preferences. Do you have a standard based on lightness? Detail your reflections below:

_____

_____

_____

_____

_____

_____

CHECKLIST

____List 4 racist beauty standards.

____Write one paragraph on the difference between fighting racism with racism and fighting racism with antiracism.

____This week, recognize when dark skin is treated differently than light skin (within the same race).

____Repeat "I will not judge someone based on lightness or darkness" seven times every morning this week.

CHAPTER 10 - WHITE

I explained that I had figured out what makes people the way they are. My friend returned a look of incredulity and told me to proceed in telling him my new, bright ideas. It wasn't my mission to figure out white people when I arrived at college, it was to figure out the black identity. I recall writing about black positivity being a new experience at college in an early English composition class. I ignored all the black positivity from back home simply because it was different. I was being racist and not antiracist.

Later that day, we stood around waiting for the result of the 2000 election in early November. We desperately wanted to keep our Governor's brother from entering the white house, especially after he put an end to affirmative action legislation in Florida. Al Gore won and we were victorious!

For a short while, anyway. It seems that Florida was too close of a race to call officially. I awoke the next morning to learn that George's brother had appointed people to recount the votes. The result was devastating, especially on top of all the actions that were taken to suppress the black vote in the months leading up to the pivotal election. My anger was overwhelming but I found no comfort in it. Almost 180,000 black votes were suppressed in Florida alone and the Bush victory was only a few hundred votes, with his brother's minions in charge of the count. This was undeniably the power of racism, which mainstream journalists readily admitted. It was like watching a scary movie, a horror that I could not turn away from even if I wanted to.

Bush took the White House early the next year and I took to hating white people. I still had work to do to figure out why white people were this way. I read a retelling of history which I had not heard of before. It told of an ancient time in a world with all black people that had turned evil when a mad scientist used selective breeding to create white people over six centuries. He then unleashed these pale savages and turned the black utopia into a warring Hell on Earth. This mythos was the reverse of what I heard about white saviors civilizing black savages while growing up.

While reading this racist retelling of history, I started to feel excited and scared. It was like I held the forbidden apple from the garden of Eden in my hands. I trembled and consumed it. I greedily devoured the new knowledge which vindicated my history with and hatred of white people. This creationist story took hold in a young man nicknamed Satan. Satan's name was actually Malcolm Little, who would become Malcolm X. Malcolm also took to this creationist revision and ran with it, spreading the Nation of Islam. I continued to read the history, enthralled by it. Malcolm took these ideas originating with Elijah Muhammad and sharpened them. Then, years later, he took a pilgrimage to mecca and converted from the Nation to Orthodox Islam. He plainly rejected Elijah's teachings and said they did not represent Islam. He also faced the fact that black people can be racist towards white people, a fact that is still not readily faced today.

We must never mistake hatred of white racism for the hatred of white people. We must never attribute the actions of white racists to white people in general. To be antiracist means that the individual is responsible only for the individual. We must also never confuse antiracism for anti-white racism.

White nationalism and white supremacists actually support racist policies which hurt white people. They are against state welfare programs which help support their fellow white person. They are against job quotas which help white women get jobs. They are generally against policies to address global warming, which negatively affects the planet that white people live on. White supremacists in many ways are anti-white.

I told my roommate none of the above. I told him that white people are aliens. I told him that this explained their anti-human level behavior and drive to dominate as a race. My roommate told me that white people and black people can reproduce together, which is unlikely for aliens and humans. No matter what, I knew that white people were different we were better off stopping our attempts to change them. I wrote in the school paper that white people were just being themselves and were afraid of extinction since their genes are not dominant. This caused quite an uproar in the community. The editor of the local paper called me in for a discussion. I was an intern there and needed his approval for graduation.

KNOWLEDGE RETENTION TEST

1. George Bush was the first person to be declared the winner of the 2000 presidential election.

   True   [ ]

   False [X]

2. White racism should be attributed to white individuals.

   True   [ ]

   False [X]

3. Black people can be racist towards white people.

   True [X]

   False [ ]

4. The beliefs of white nationalists hurt white people.

   True [X]

   False [ ]

5. To be anti-white is to be racist.

   True [X]

   False [ ]

PREP WORK Q & A

1. What is your experience with racism from and against white people?

    _____

    _____

    _____

    _____

    _____

2. Explain how anti-black white nationalists and anti-white black Nation of Islam members actually hurt their own race? Working out this concept is key to arguing for an antiracist society since individuals tend to want what is in the best interest of their own group.

    _____

    _____

    _____

    _____

    _____

3. When we are attacked, we want to attack back with equal and opposite force. This is not the path to being an antiracist. Develop a sentence/mantra you can say to yourself that will remind you that individuals do not represent their racial group.

    _____

    _____

    _____

    _____

    _____

CHECKLIST

___Reflect on your own experience with whiteness.

___Remember that racism against the majority is still racism.

___Develop a mantra to remind yourself to treat individuals as individuals.

___Use that mantra when an individual attacks you or your race to make sure you don't emulate their racism.

CHAPTER 11 - BLACK

The editor listed off criticisms of my piece and we went back and forth for what felt like hours. He could sense my anger but respected my ability to remain calm and debate my points. The conversation was enjoyable until he said that he hated getting stereotyped like one of those 'n' words' (fully articulated).

Chris rock had popularized this sentiment in his HBO special. He described the difference between black people and nig---rs. The bit was met with applause and laughter. Rock eventually stopped performing this part of the act when he noticed that white people enjoyed the bit a bit too much. Rock was just exposing the ugly truth how many black people felt. They had internalized the racism of racist policy. In recent years, polls have shown that a majority of black people blame factors other than racism for inequality between the races. This is internalized racism and it has a long history.

One could point to Hannibal Thomas, a man who so desperately wanted to fit in with the white majority that he took to disparaging black people as inferior, savage beings. The *New York Times* respected him as an authority on black people, second only to Booker T. Washington. However, his use did not work for the racist agenda. Black people considered him the equal of Brutus or Judas, a betrayer. Since white people couldn't use him anymore, they discarded him entirely and he had to find manual labor until he died years later without many people noticing.

Under the Reagan administration, the number of discrimination cases that were dropped increased significantly. The amount of housing provided to non-whites dropped substantially. This set the stage for future racist policies under the Trump administration. Ben Carson would add himself to the list of politicians to use anti-black racist policies against other black people.

The editor gave me the ultimatum of ending my column at the school newspaper or ending my internship. I chose to end my column in the school paper and I felt like a part of me died with it. However, it was a part of me that needed to die. The racist part. I started studying African American studies as my second major and changed for the better.

KNOWLEDGE RETENTION TEST

1. People rarely use racial slurs against people of their own race in a derogatory way.

   True   [ ]

   False   [X]

2. Black people internalized racial ideas from white racist policy.

   True   [X]

   False   [ ]

3. Comedians expose ugliness about humanity, consciously or otherwise.

   True   [X]

   False [ ]

4. Racists will use you as an authority if you speak out against your own race but will likely discard you when you no longer serve a purpose, because it's about power.

   True   [X]

   False [ ]

5. It's easy to kill off the racist part of ourselves.

   True   [ ]

   False [X]

PREP WORK Q & A

1. We can become intimate with our anger and use it as a means of security. Can you write about an angry part of yourself which you had to let die?

   _____

   _____

   _____

   _____

   _____

2. Laughing at racial tensions can seem like a way to end them but often it just reveals something we need to work on. Would you consider Chris Rock's skit racist or antiracist based on the definitions we've established?

   _____

   _____

   _____

   _____

   _____

3. What's a slur used against your race and have you ever used it against another member of your race. How will you change in light of the lessons of this chapter?

   _____

   _____

   _____

   _____

   _____

CHECKLIST

___Develop your own peaceful ways of calming anger which spawns from racial tensions so you can be antiracist and not racist.

___Do not attack your own race as a means of fitting in with another race.

___Remember that those who perpetuate intra-racial hierarchy are promoting racism.

___Look at the races of individuals you invite to group gatherings. If you treat people as individuals, there should be some amount of racial equality in the numbers.

FUN BREAK 2 OF 3

Wow your making great progress, keep it up. This crossword puzzle is a little harder than your last puzzle. Do your best to solve it without using the answer sheet on the next page. Once you're done let's get back to learning.

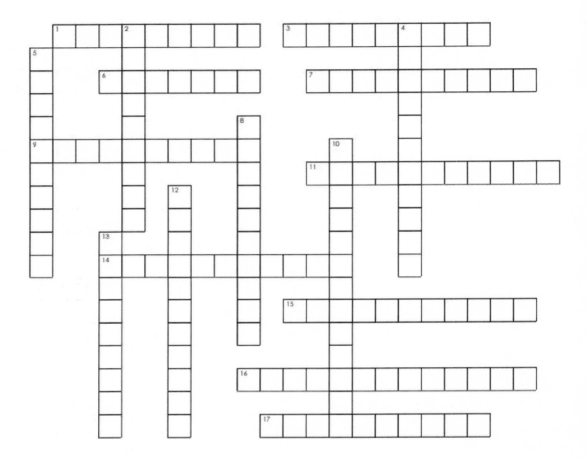

<u>Across:</u> →
1. A final demand or statement of terms
3. To clear someone of suspicion
6. The ability to share others feelings
7. A preconceived notion about someone
9. A long journey to some sacred place
11. Something that is your job or duty
14. Being unwilling to believe something
15. The author of this book
16. relating to several ethnic groups
17. A remarkable person thing or event

<u>Down:</u> ↓
2. Someone who lives in a foreign land
4. Someone who believes in divine creation
5. having a dislike for homosexual people
8. To make something continue indefinitely
10. A exhibition of how something works
12. The forced separation of racial groups
13. The ranking of people 1 above the other

FUN BREAK 2 OF 3 ANSWER SHEET

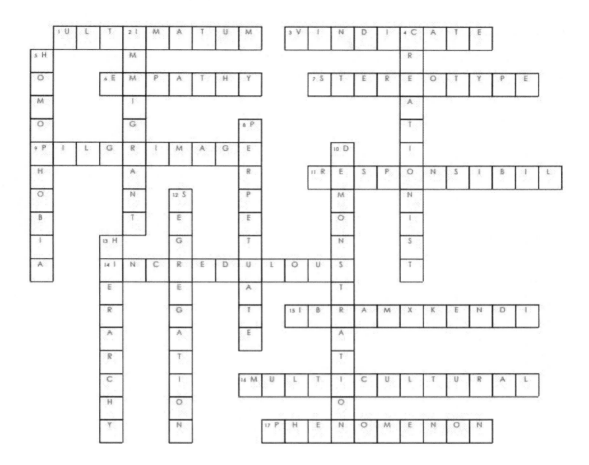

Across: →

1. A final demand or statement of terms
3. To clear someone of suspicion
6. The ability to share others feelings
7. A preconceived notion about someone
9. A long journey to some sacred place
11. Something that is your job or duty
14. Being unwilling to believe something
15. The author of this book
16. relating to several ethnic groups
17. A remarkable person thing or event

Down: ↓

2. Someone who lives in a foreign land
4. Someone who believes in divine creation
5. having a dislike for homosexual people
8. To make something continue indefinitely
10. A exhibition of how something works
12. The forced separation of racial groups
13. The ranking of people 1 above the other

CHAPTER 12 - CLASS

I moved up North to Philly to study at Temple University in the middle of the 2000s. I was excited to learn from my new major. The building I stayed in looked like no one could possibly live in it. The bodies moving by outside my window had no idea that there was a living person above them.

My neighbors told me how dangerous the neighborhood was, with the highest crime rates. It's here that I got the sense of the intersectionality of race and class. To think blacks are inferior is racist. To think poor people are inferior is classist or elitist. To think the poor blacks are especially inferior is both racist and elitist. Poor and black combined to be a race-class combination. Poor whites also suffer from class racism when they are called terms like white trash. Just like with racism, whoever sets the standard for this intersection also determines the hierarchy.

Welfare has been blamed for this poverty. Poor whites and poor blacks alike are degraded by the dependency on these programs. By using welfare, it's argued, they turned themselves from being of agency to dependent beasts without the drive to be self-reliant. President Obama made such a claim of defeat based on discrimination, that it had left generations of black people unmotivated to join the economic process and achieve the American dream. Black elites, like white elites, tend to think of themselves as having more than just a greater salary. They think of themselves a better type of person, which is reflected in their salary.

Spain's conquest of the 'New World'' gave birth to racism and capitalism. The babies stayed safe and began to grow as Europeans slaughtered the Native Americans in mass genocide and established their empires in the new territories. The black poverty rate is twice that of white Americans. Black wealth is expected to reach a median of 0 over the next few decades. Black poverty stands out more than white poverty as black poverty tends to be dense. This also means that poor black people have to compete with each other for resources. Poor white Americans are scattered in their poverty, spread among richer whites.

I realize now that I had moved to one of these poor, dense black areas in a racist fashion. I stereotyped poor black people the same way as racist whites and elitist, racist blacks. However, I saw the existence as romantic and authentic. I wanted that pure black experience and I ran towards using the neighborhood to get it.

KNOWLEDGE RETENTION TEST

1. Bad neighborhoods get their reputations through objective measurements and not racist ideas.

   True   [ ]

   False [X]

2. White elites tend to think of themselves as a better type of person.

   True   [X]

   False [ ]

3. Black elites tend to think of themselves as a better type of person.

   True   [X]

   False [ ]

4. Black median wealth is expected to rise in the next few decades.

   True   [ ]

   False [ ]

5. White poverty is denser in its distribution.

   True   [ ]

   False [X]

PREP WORK Q & A

1. The intersection of race and class is a form of identity caused by racism and classism. Identify three race-classes which are prevalent in your neighborhood.

   _____

   _____

   _____

   _____

   _____

2. Working out the balance between individuality and antiracism is a necessary step in moving away from racism. How do 'progressive' arguments explaining black disengagement actually promote racism?

   _____

   _____

   _____

   _____

   _____

3. How would a class-racist describe your race-class and why is this inaccurate?

   _____

   _____

   _____

   _____

   _____

CHECKLIST

___Remember to treat your neighborhood by your day to day interaction with individuals and not by the race-class assumptions of outsiders.

___At the same time, take into account the inequities different race classes suffer from.

___Make sure to vote against local policies which target race-classes negatively.

___Promote local policies which create equality for race-classes which need equality.

CHAPTER 13 - SPACE

We explicitly called our spaces where we studied African American studies black spaces. Most of the bodies were black as was the shared culture. The rest of the spaces at the university were white spaces but they did not label them as such. They pretended to be neutral in race, but this lie of blindness did little to mask the truth of the whiteness of the space.

Molefi Asante argued for a return to an African-centric way of thinking. He argued that many people thought they were seeing the world through a multicultural lens but that they were truly seeing the world through a European multicultural lens. The filter of Europe was distorting the lens and you had to get in touch with a purer, Afrocentric clarity to really see the world as a black person. You have to fight through years of European influence.

Professor Mazama was a force to be reckoned with, despite her soft voice. In fact, her effective soft spokenness taught me the value of words for their own sake. One need not be boisterous to make a point. She also once stumped me with the proposition that there's no such thing as objectivity, only an agreed-upon subjectivity. When asked what to do if there is no subjectivity, she answered that one needed only to tell their truth.

Black neighborhoods are stigmatized as 'dangerous' because you might be robbed and attacked. This stigma ignores the fact that white-collar criminals will steal your entire life's savings while smiling at you. How you perceive locations changes how those locations operate. We falsely identify spaces until they become what we fear, or what we secretly want. A space becomes racialized when racist ideas influence it.

It's all too easy for a space to get a bad reputation. At Temple, we talked about our undergraduate studies and the colleges we attended. There was only one other FAMU alumni in our group and she always degraded the university and shot down my attempts of pride in the university. It got on my nerves, so I pressed her on the issue. She said that someone in the transcript department messed up her transcript. Because of that, she condemned the university. This angered me even more. How could she outright condemn the entirety of our university, my university, because of one error? I was tired of hearing adults and outsiders condemn historically black colleges and universities and it was even worse to have a fellow alumni do the same. Constantly, comparisons are made between historically black colleges and the best 'white' universities as if these comparisons were fair. The funding for the richest black college was still several times less than even average white schools. Again, policy had racialized black spaces and still does to this day. This spawns from a long history of location racism. Thomas Jefferson suggested freeing slaves and sending them back to Africa with the ability to civilize the continent. Leading up to the Civil War, black leaders in Georgia were asked if black Georgians would rather be separate or integrated with white people. The leaders responded that they would rather be separate. Sherman ordered a field order for slaves to be freed to coastal land, but this didn't last long as landowners started to 'take back' the otherwise unused land. Segregation led to underperforming black schools. Again, segregation itself was blamed instead of the wide gap in funding to each school. The spaces were racialized as a causal factor of inequality.

An antiracist supports the integration of different types of bodies voluntarily and fights for equal resources and challenging racist policies which create atmospheres of inequality. However, an antiracist does not suggest that any space attributed to a single racial group will inherently have a negative effect on an individual because it is a white or black space. The spaces did not have a negative effect on me, and neither did the questions that were asked.

KNOWLEDGE RETENTION TEST

1. Black spaces are overtly black.

   True   [ ]

   False [ ]

2. White spaces disguise themselves as multiracial spaces.

   True   [x]

   False [ ]

3. Black theft is viewed as more dangerous, even when it is less damaging than white-collar crime.

   True   [x]

   False [ ]

4. It takes years of work to break through a European-centric way of viewing life.

   True   [x]

   False [ ]

5. One bad experience can give a space a bad reputation.

   True   [x]

   False [ ]

PREP WORK Q & A

1. Think of a space you believe to be dangerous without ever having been there. How might a day there change your mind?

_____

_____

_____

_____

_____

_____

2. How is your own moral filter affected by European colonialism and conquest?

_____

_____

_____

_____

_____

_____

3. Explain how a racialized space can still promote equality and antiracism.

_____

_____

_____

_____

_____

_____

CHECKLIST

____Don't believe a space is dangerous without personal investigation.

____Support voluntarily integrated spaced which supply equality.

____Support racialized spaces if those spaces create equality of opportunity.

____Judge the funding of a racialized space before judging the race-class.

CHAPTER 14 - GENDER

Kaila was literally and figuratively a towering intellect that did not try to hide her lesbian side or feminist wit. Space for black people aren't always welcoming to gay people or feminists, but that didn't cause a moment's hesitation in her. She would tell you what she thought of you without hesitation or apology. She could do a dead-on impersonation of students and have everyone laughing at the accuracy. I always half desired, half feared her doing an impression of me. You had to respect her. The remaining choice was to fear her or to battle her, and most chose fear.

I was not the ideal candidate to befriend Kaila as I was as homophobic as I was racist and as racist as I was ignorant. I always felt my lack of mental prowess around her. However, she still felt I had some potential. My parents did not explicitly raise me to be homophobic, but they didn't actually teach me to be anti-homophobic. It wasn't really brought up in our household which is in itself homophobic. We didn't exactly have typical gender roles as my father was an emotional man and my mother always showed signs of strength and toughness. However, when it came down to it, my mother would yield that my father was the head of the household.

When an interracial group of critics came out condemning black mothers for raising children alone, on mostly faulty statistics, my parents joined in the criticism. My mother spoke out more on a few other feminist issues. When the pastor was going over their vows, my mother took issue with the line about obeying her husband. My father and the priest were stunned, but my father relented and suggested that the line changed to a mutual submission to each other. My mother quite liked this and agreed to the change.

Black women had to organize to fight the sexism within black spaces and the racism in white spaces. It was a war fought on two fronts for the liberation of black women. Gender racism is when a policy or idea creates inequities for black women, black men, or any combination of race and gender.

You can't be antiracist, in purity, without also being a feminist. The same is true of the reverse. For evidence of gendered racism against black women, you could look at the hundreds of thousands of black women who were sterilized in throughout the 20th century. You can also look at the fact that the median income for black women is almost 0 while the median income for white women is 44,000. This is a result of racist and sexist policy.

Intersectionality explores the unique circumstances of oppression that each group experiences. This is a blessing, as one can begin to understand the set of policies that have affected every group. This exploration is a must for any antiracist. For all the levels of racism I was learning to explore, I still had much work to do on gender and that education started at Temple with Kaila.

KNOWLEDGE RETENTION TEST

1. You can be an antiracist without being a feminist.

   True   [ ]

   False [X]

2. Households which do not discuss homophobia actually promote homophobia.

   True   [X]

   False [ ]

3. Black women have to fight sexism in black spaces and racism in white spaces.

   True   [X]

   False [ ]

4. You can't be a feminist without being an antiracist.

   True   [X]

   False [ ]

5. Gender racism is when a policy or idea creates inequalities for black women, black men, or any combination of race and gender.

   True   [X]

   False [ ]

PREP WORK Q & A

1. Racism and sexism are usually seen as two separate issues. Can you use lessons from the chapter and your own experience to detail how they are connected at the level of intersectionality?

_____

_____

_____

_____

_____

2. Class racism can combine with gender racism. Can you name two ways in which a poor, race-gendered person might suffer discrimination worse than a rich person of the same race-gender?

_____

_____

_____

_____

_____

3. How does your focus on the injustices in your own life leave you blind to the plight of others and how will you open your eyes to this?

_____

_____

_____

_____

_____

CHECKLIST

___Remember that you can't be antiracist without being feminist.

___Evaluate how you treat different race-genders in your own life and correct for equality.

___Make sure you apply the same effort towards equality for all races to equality for all genders, including all race-gender combinations.

___Make sure equality for one race doesn't create inequality in a race-gender.

FUN BREAK 3 OF 3

You've made it to the final fun break. This one will really test your skill. The words below are all from this book and can be hidden across, down, diagonal and backwards. Enjoy the final fun break then let's get back to learning. (Answer sheet on next page)

```
B C Q Z W X P T L M O X M V I O L E N C E Z O
I O R F H H E F V M E R I Y G O L O I B E E T
M L E P I Z R O F G N E C X X K Y N B P S N N
M O V I T G C Y I C G S R X C Y H O L F I S E
I R E E E O T N E A P O R O M C I A S H L M
G L I T N R P I C T G O A O L C R T I S C A N
R A H A E O T C R A E N G I O Z A A C E N U E
A I C L S T I I E U M S G V N O R N I N A T T
N C A A S A O N D T E I R A I F E U F K R C H
T A R C C D N H U E N B E H A F I L R C F E G
E R E S H E E T L P T I S E L E H U E A N L I
N R D E S R H E I R O L S B I N U Z P L E L L
T E N E T P P A T E A I I C S D A T U B S E N
A T U D D E P F Y P M T O Q M E O G S K I T E
U N Q G C U L T U R E Y N X Z R E I G Y D N K
K I E B O N I C S E P Y T O E R E T S T P I T
```

Find the following words in the puzzle.
Words are hidden ↑ ↓ → ← and ↘ .

BEHAVIOR
BIOLOGY
BLACKNESS
COLONIALISM
COLOR
CULTURE
DEESCALATE
DISENFRANCHISE

EBONICS
ENGAGEMENT
ENLIGHTENMENT
ETHNICITY
HIERARCHY
IMMIGRANT
INCREDULITY
INTELLECTUALS

INTERRACIAL
MICROAGGRESSION
OFFENDER
PERCEPTION
PERPETUATE
PREDATOR
RESPONSIBILITY
STEREOTYPE

SUPERFICIAL
UNDERACHIEVER
VIOLENCE
WHITENESS
ZULUNATION

```
.  C  .  .  W  .  P  .  .  .  .  .  M  V  I  O  L  E  N  C  E  .  .
I  O  R  .  H  .  E  .  .  .  E  R  I  Y  G  O  L  O  I  B  E  .  T
M  L  E  .  I  .  R  .  .  .  N  E  C  .  .  .  Y  N  .  .  S  .  N
M  O  V  .  T  .  C  Y  I  .  G  S  R  .  C  .  H  O  L  .  I  S  E
I  R  E  E  E  .  E  T  N  E  A  P  O  R  O  .  C  I  A  S  H  L  M
G  L  I  T  N  R  P  I  C  T  G  O  A  O  L  .  R  T  I  S  C  A  N
R  A  H  A  E  O  T  C  R  A  E  N  G  I  O  .  A  A  C  E  N  U  E
A  I  C  L  S  T  I  I  E  U  M  S  G  V  N  O  R  N  I  N  A  T  T
N  C  A  A  S  A  O  N  D  T  E  I  R  A  I  F  E  U  F  K  R  C  H
T  A  R  C  .  D  N  H  U  E  N  B  E  H  A  F  I  L  R  C  F  E  G
.  R  E  S  .  E  .  T  L  P  T  I  S  E  L  E  H  U  E  A  N  L  I
.  R  D  E  .  R  .  E  I  R  .  L  S  B  I  N  .  Z  P  L  E  L  L
.  E  N  E  .  P  .  .  T  E  .  I  I  .  S  D  .  .  U  B  S  E  N
.  T  U  D  .  .  .  .  Y  P  .  T  O  .  M  E  .  .  S  .  I  T  E
.  N  .  .  C  U  L  T  U  R  E  Y  N  .  .  R  .  .  .  .  D  N  .
.  I  E  B  O  N  I  C  S  E  P  Y  T  O  E  R  E  T  S  .  .  I  .
```

Word directions and start points are formatted: (Direction, X, Y)

BEHAVIOR (E,14,7)
BIOLOGY (E,14,16)
BLACKNESS (E,5,15)
COLONIALISM (E,4,12)
COLOR (SE,15,11)
CULTURE (E,7,10)
DEESCALATE (W,22,2)
DISENFRANCHISE (S,2,1)

EBONICS (E,14,8)
ENGAGEMENT (E,6,14)
ENLIGHTENMENT (SE,7,2)
ETHNICITY (SE,3,3)
HIERARCHY (N,22,16)
IMMIGRANT (N,21,16)
INCREDULITY (SE,10,4)
INTELLECTUALS (E,10,5)

INTERRACIAL (W,16,13)
MICROAGGRESSION (SE,4,1)
OFFENDER (SE,6,2)
PERCEPTION (W,17,3)
PERPETUATE (S,1,3)
PREDATOR (N,4,9)
RESPONSIBILITY (S,3,2)
STEREOTYPE (E,9,1)

SUPERFICIAL (W,13,16)
UNDERACHIEVER (W,23,4)
VIOLENCE (N,6,11)
WHITENESS (E,13,6)
ZULUNATION (S,23,5)

CHAPTER 15 - SEXUALITY

Just as there are race-genders, there are also race-sexualities. Homosexuality is a sexuality. A gay Asian person is a race-sexuality. Ideas and policies that create inequities between race-sexualities are what is known as queer racism. A disproportionate number of children raised by same-sex couples suffer because of queer racism. These policies are hindering the development of these children.

You might believe that racism and homophobia are separate issues. However, they've been intertwined throughout history and are inseparable. Havelock Ellis is the physician responsible for popularizing the term homosexual. He also championed the idea that people are born criminals, not turned into criminals through socialization, and that black people were naturally inclined to criminal activity. He intersected race and sexuality by comparing the tamed clitoris of white women with the prominent clitoris in black women, and suggested that lesbian black women will always have a noticeably large clitoris. Black people have always been suggested as being more sexual than white people. Similarly, homosexuals have long been described as being more sexual than heterosexuals. Thus, the black queer is seen as the most sexual beast of them all through the intersection of racism and homophobia.

Weckea was another friend at Temple who I looked up to. Like Kaila, he had a burning curiosity to know and discuss everything. He also loved to laugh. His temperament was more laid back than mine, which is usually the type of friend I was drawn to. Another one of our friends, Raena, rounded out a trio. One day I was at lunch with Raena without Weckea and she told me that Weckea was gay. It was a bit of a surprise to me because I thought of Weckea as conservative and my mind associated gay black men as sexual deviants, having rampant unprotected sex. I thought about how this spread AIDS in the black community. My thoughts were very wrong. Black gay men use condoms more often than white gay men and are less likely to use drugs during sex, reducing risk. The racist, homophobic idea that I had about the sexuality of the black queer was being called into question by Raena's comment. This was an awakening to me. I began to learn that some gay men prefer to act masculine and that others act feminine. I say 'act' because peers like Kaila were teaching me that gender is a performance of social constructs without ties to biology.

I was more concerned with why my friend didn't tell me about this aspect of himself. Whenever I brought up girls, he would talk about who he thought was pretty. It was never in a sexual manner, I realized after the fact. He would deflect whenever I brought up girls that he dated. I thought this was part of his conservative nature, but really, he was hiding a part of himself to me. Later in life, he would show off his gaydar to me. This was his ability to point out closeted gay people and another ability to sense homophobia. He must have sensed my own homophobia and protected our friendship by keeping his sexuality a secret.

I had to make a choice between my homophobia and my friend. I chose my friend and bonded through lifelong friendship. That time with the graduate student forced me to change much about my homophobic and patriarchal ways. My ideas about gender and sexuality really stood no chance against their intellect and persuasion and I was forced to change towards the truth.

KNOWLEDGE RETENTION TEST

1. You can be antiracist and still be homophobic.

   True [ ]

   False [X]

2. White gay men use condoms more than black gay men.

   True [ ]

   False [X]

3. Black gay men are primarily responsible for spreading AIDS.

   True [ ]

   False [X]

4. Friendships will force you to choose between being homophobic and being a hypocrite.

   True [ ]

   False [X]

5. Friendships will force you to choose between being racist and being a hypocrite.

   True [ ]

   False [X]

PREP WORK Q & A

1. Friendships force us to face our racist, homophobic, and sexist ideas or live as a hypocrite. Can you recall a friend who made you challenge prejudicial ideas through their behavior?

_____

_____

_____

_____

_____

2. Take a look at your current friend group. Are they challenging you to be better on any of these issues?

_____

_____

_____

_____

_____

3. Have you ever identified with your socially prescribed race-sexuality? How was this experience?

_____

_____

_____

_____

CHECKLIST

____Remember that racism goes beyond just race.

____Fight against homophobia with equal fervor as racism.

____Make a list of your beliefs on race, gender, and sexuality and check for hypocrisy so you might correct it.

____Make sure you have friends who are challenging you to improve on all levels of ethics.

CHAPTER 16 - FAILURE

It was the fall of 2007 and I sat anxiously as people gathered. I couldn't remain seated and I couldn't remain sitting. I wanted to get started. Lives hung in the balance and there was no time to wait. I was ready to present the plan to save those young lives but I was always destined to fail. Racism is alive and well today because antiracism has been fraught with failure. We have largely failed to create societies of antiracism. These failures are always felt and they echo into future generations.

We tend to ignore this impact because we view race incorrectly. We view it as a single upward slope towards progress rather than a contest between the racist and the antiracist. We view race as a social phenomenon rather than a power construct. Education and mentoring programs help to create strong individuals but they fail to fix bad policy and will ultimately fail on a group level.

We repeat these memes, even though they fail to work over and over again. The black person is charged with acting moral to represent the entire race, an impossible task, and is shamed and disproportionately punished when he or she fails to meet this standard.

I'd been dating my girlfriend for several months and I was already thinking about marrying her. Her perceptiveness, sense of humor, grace, and love for saving others as a physician made her stand out to me. People told her she was also a shining example for the race. She internalized this. One day we were out to lunch and we saw a white man acting drunk and disorderly, fondling a religious statue. She was glad that he wasn't black, commenting how bad it would make them look. She believed the actions of the individual represent the race. As we left the lunch, we continued to talk about why we had internalized these judgments and whether or not it was fair for the individual to have to rise to the higher standards of racists.

Black people are constantly forced down by bad policy and ordered to uplift themselves again through good behavior. It's a cycle that is doomed to fail. In the end, I am responsible for myself and my actions. I do not represent black people. White individuals do not represent white people.

Power and opportunism are often disguised as progress. For instance, the Civil Rights acts of the 1960s did just enough to calm American foreign policy relations. A history of religious and racial discrimination was hurting Americas ability to operate in overseas markets. Once enough fears were calmed and enough people were appeased, progress halted.

We had gathered to help free the Jena 6 who were facing charges for assaulting a young white male. They were 6 black teens and the attack came months after nooses were hung from trees by white students. The prosecution was seeking unfair sentences for the boys, disproportionate to the lenient treatment given to white students involved in similar attacks and threats.

I couldn't wait for the remainder of the individuals to convene any longer so I began to detail my plan; to have students from around the country gather and protest. The protests would act as fundraisers to fund the defense team for the 6 boys. Furthermore, I planned a sit in on Washington that included parking caravans around the capital. We would pressure Washington into freeing the Jena 6. In my mind, it was a beautiful plan. I was an out-of-control radical trying to channel my inner Civil Rights leader and did so foolishly. I failed to change the minds of anyone in the room. I had failed miserably, but I blamed my failure on the ignorance of my audience and not my own misconceptions about the situation. Demonstrations without real policy change are fruitless. They only act to discourage policy change and demoralize those who would be active. You need to grasp power, not just protest against it.

KNOWLEDGE RETENTION TEST

1. Punishments for children are historically colorblind.

   True   [ ]

   False [X]

2. Black individuals represent black people.

   True   [ ]

   False [X]

3. White individuals represent white people.

   True   [ ]

   False [X]

4. You must gain antiracist power to fight racist power.

   True   [X]

   False [ ]

5. Black individuals must work not to be embarrassed by the actions of other black individuals.

   True   [X]

   False [ ]

PREP WORK Q & A

1. Detail a time where you were embarrassed by a member of the same race, thinking that they made the entire race look bad. How can you confront this embarrassment for its racism?

   _____

   _____

   _____

   _____

   _____

2. Why is gaining antiracist power better than protesting?

   _____

   _____

   _____

   _____

   _____

3. Why do education and mentoring programs fail to address the core issue? What's something you can do over the next five years to gain antiracist power to help create an antiracist world?

   _____

   _____

   _____

   _____

   _____

CHECKLIST

___Realize that failures are a learning experience.

___Gain your own power instead of protesting the power of others.

___Do not hold individuals to a standard other than their own potential.

___Antiracist policy is often an opportunistic power grab by lawmakers – be weary.

CHAPTER 17 - SUCCESS

I sat in the auditorium listening to Boyce Watkins teach his theory of racism as a disorder during a meeting for Black History month at Temple. I had just enjoyed receiving my doctoral degree just a few weeks earlier. Yes, the kid who struggled with school ended up completing the highest level of graduate education. I shot my hand up after the lecture, during the Q and A section. I wasn't buying into the theory. My friend Caridad gave an exciting smirk in the seat next to me as I confidently thrust my hand into the air. She had brought me into the graduate program and I took up her husband's post in the Black history department when her husband left. She has been through quite a lot but she is a warrior, as one must be to succeed in the quest of antiracism.

Success is the goal we strive towards, ever-elusive. Success for the antiracist is a world where power and policy support equality of opportunity for all. This equality of opportunity will produce equality of outcome. This world can often feel far away and each person might fight a personal battle against the antiracist ideas that have been ingrained in them. Caridad would always leave me with positive messages so I wouldn't fall back into my racist thoughts upon my departure from Temple.

My retort to the speaker was that racism was more like an organ than a disease. I did not get him to debate me, even with my rejection of his thesis. I was ready to spar. Not because I was an intellectual but because I knew I would get to validate my opinions. I was shut off to ideas that didn't make me feel good, so I fortified my own ideas.

I began to think of the system of racism that was keeping black people down. I could never fully grasp how this system worked as a whole. I knew it existed because I could see the policy it produced. I wanted to fully understand this system of racism so I could help prevent its systemic nature. The fact that you could not pin down this system to single individuals and prove their intent made it difficult to wake people up and take action. We need a villain to take out to get us mobilized, and we rarely have just one fully culpable individual.

I doubled down in my quest to figure out racism by going through the history books and noting *every* instance of racism I could find. The notes piled up fast, into the thousands. I felt their negative energy. They were toxic and it was a dark time. However, it also helped me recognize the racism that was still alive within me. It was therapeutic once I got those notes onto the page. I realized how far I had come and how far left I still had to go. I had to acknowledge myself as a racist and write down the ways I was a racist and why I was this way. These are the necessary steps to become an antiracist. So, my question to understand racism in America led to my discovery of the racist within myself and how deep those roots went.

I still struggle to see things through an antiracist mind. I let false studies sway me, think in general terms about individual actions, fall back on biological racial memes, forget the importance of intersectionality, but now I am aware of the process. I decided to change. Racist ideas had embarrassed me for my entire life. It was time to put an end to it.

KNOWLEDGE RETENTION TEST

1. The point of a debate is to win.

    True   [ ]
    False [X]   *arrive at truth*

2. Success is about feeling better about ourselves.

    True   [ ]
    False [ ]

3. Falsely living in anger can lead to a therapeutic revelation away from anger.

    True   [X]
    False [ ]

4. Systems of racism are uncomplicated and easy to understand and identify.

    True   [ ]
    False [X]

5. You must first accept that you are a racist before becoming an antiracist.

    True   [X]
    False [ ]

PREP WORK Q & A

1. Recall a time when you wanted to win an argument rather than arrive at the truth.

   _____

   _____

   _____

   _____

   _____

2. We're not close to an antiracist world but we can still work on it. What's something you can uniquely contribute to this fight?

   _____

   _____

   _____

   _____

   _____

3. We must all accept that we are racist before becoming an antiracist. Please list the ways in which you are racist below. Then, declare how you will fight these ideas.

   _____

   _____

   _____

   _____

   _____

CHECKLIST

____Fight the urge to 'win' an argument rather than arrive at new understandings.

____Realize that you've been embarrassing yourself by not progressing and decide to put an end to it.

____Accept that you are a racist.

____Make a list of every racist idea you have and take action to correct these ideas.

CHAPTER 18 - SURVIVAL

Sadiqa and I had just moved into our new apartment. We had married suddenly and had a beautiful ceremony which we were still high off of. She felt a lump on one of her breasts. She thought it was nothing because she was much too young to have breast cancer. I urged her to get it checked out and she did have it looked at that day.

Her mother wailed over the phone when I told her that her daughter had breast cancer. Her daughter didn't have the heart to tell her. They both cried as I anguished inside. Eventually, we calmed down and began to process our options. We wanted to have her embryos frozen in the case her ovaries were damaged by chemo. This process caused a blood clot which delayed her surgery. She was in a fight before she could even begin to fight the cancer. She had just finished medical school and now had to be a patient instead of treating her own. She was in for the longest fight of our lives.

She won.

During the struggle, it was difficult for me to separate my anger towards racism from my anger towards the cancer. The two became the same in my body, emotionally. Racism is a type of cancer though, isn't it? Think of how fast and suddenly it spread since its inception a few hundred years ago. It's taken over the globe and threatens to take over civilization. It affects every part of the body. We are currently in stage 4 of the cancer's growth.

Soon after, a mass was found in my colon. I too had cancer. Stage 4. The odds were not good as the survival rate was just over ten percent. I had to fight just like we have to fight against racism with all that we have, despite the poor odds. I made a plan and moved forward. I kept writing this book even as the chemotherapy attacked me and the cancer. I stuck to my chemo plan and used the pain as a healing mechanism. I had surgery and, for now, the cancer is gone.

The chances aren't very good. However, we can give it all we have. My wife fought against the odds and won. We can fight against the cancer that is racism and give the world a chance at an antiracist home. We are only guaranteed to lose to racism when we quit completely. We must look at our failures on the road to success as momentary setbacks and not a reason to give up. If we keep striving towards our goal, we might one day be free.

KNOWLEDGE RETENTION TEST

1. There's no point in fighting an improbable fight. You should just accept reality peacefully.

    True   [ ]

    False [x]

2. You should fight battles that are worth fighting with all that you have.

    True   [x]

    False [ ]

3. Racism is like a cancer.

    True   [x]

    False [ ]

4. Our chances of defeating racism aren't very good.

    True   [ ]

    False [ ]

5. Personal battles often reflect social conflicts.

    True   [x]

    False [ ]

PREP WORK Q & A

1. Name a time when bad news drastically changed your perspective on life. Can you channel that sobering experience to help fight racism? Why or why not?

_____

_____

_____

_____

_____

_____

2. Fighting racism will take a great deal of your energy. Years worth. Is an antiracist world worth fighting for? Are you ready for this?

_____

_____

_____

_____

_____

_____

3. Describe a time when you overcame near-impossible odds.

_____

_____

_____

_____

_____

CHECKLIST

____Fighting racism will take everything you have.

____You have to be fully dedicated to this change.

____Remember that it's okay to fail along the way towards an antiracist society.

____Overcome the odds. Keep pushing towards the vision of a better tomorrow.

Congratulations, you have completed the How to Be an Antiracist Workbook

ABOUT GROWTH HACK BOOKS

Here at Growth Hack Books our goal is to save you time by providing the best workbooks possible. We stand out from our competitors by not only including all of the pertinent facts from the subject book but also knowledge retention tests after each chapter, a Prep work Q & A section after each chapter that allows you to document the steps you will take to reach your goals, easy to follow summaries of each chapter including checklists and even puzzles and games to make learning more interesting.

As you can see, we go above and beyond to make your purchase a pleasant one. If you learned something beneficial from this book please leave a positive review so others can benefit as well. Lastly if you haven't yet make sure you purchase the subject book, How to Be an Antiracist, by visiting https://amzn.to/2zahm5b

Made in the USA
Middletown, DE
05 June 2020

96790799R00059